Collins

Easy Learning
English
Age 8-9

My name is ..... Grace ....

I am ... 7 .... years old.

I go to ... Matfeld primy .... School.

My favourite book is ....

Illustrated by Rachel Annie Bridgen

How to use this book

- Find a quiet, comfortable place to work, away from other distractions.

- Tackle one topic at a time.

- Help with reading the instructions where necessary, and ensure that your child understands what to do.

- Help and encourage your child to check their own answers as they complete each activity.

- Discuss with your child what they have learnt.

- Let your child return to their favourite pages once they have been completed, to talk about the activities.

- Reward your child with plenty of praise and encouragement.

Special features

- Parent's notes: These are divided into 'What you need to know', which explain the key English idea, and 'Taking it further', which suggest activities and encourage discussion with your child about what they have learnt. The words in bold are key words that you should focus on when talking to your child.

Published by Collins
An imprint of HarperCollinsPublishers
77–85 Fulham Palace Road
Hammersmith
London
W6 8JB

Browse the complete Collins catalogue at
www.collins.co.uk

© HarperCollinsPublishers Limited 2006

10 9 8 7 6 5 4 3 2

ISBN-13 978-0-00-721026-8
ISBN-10 0-00-721026-4

British Library Cataloguing in Publication Data
A Catalogue record for this publication is available from the British Library

Design and layout by Lodestone Publishing Limited, Uckfield, East Sussex; www.lodestonepublishing.com
Illustrated by Rachel Annie Bridgen;
www.shootingthelight.com
Printed and bound by Printing Express, Hong Kong

Contents

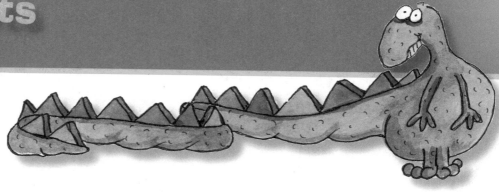

Prefixes

- Write un- in front of these words to make them mean 'not'.

  _____fastened   _____

  _____true   _____

  _____lucky   _____

  _____tidy   _____

  _____grateful   _____

- Now cover each word and write it in full.

Choosing un- words

- Choose from the un- words above to fill the spaces.

My big sister had lots of ribbons and things hanging round her mirror, and it looked very _____, so yesterday I tidied it for her. I _____ all the ribbons and threw them away.

   I thought she'd be pleased, but she was very _____. She said they were good luck charms, and it was _____ to put them in the bin. She said I only did it to annoy her. But it's _____ – I was only trying to help.

What you need to know   How to build words with common prefixes.
A prefix is a group of letters that can be added to the beginning of a word to change its meaning.

4

Super- means big

super = big above more than

- Write super- in front of these words to change their meaning. Then cover each word and write it in full.

_____ store   _____

_____ natural   _____

_____ hero   _____

_____ vise   _____

- Now match the words to these meanings.

a store which is bigger than most   _____

a hero with more-than-ordinary powers   _____

something which is beyond nature   _____

watch over other people's work   _____

Pre- means before

- Write pre- in front of these words.
  Then draw a line to the right meaning.

_____ pare   food cooked before you plan to eat it

_____ fix   say what will happen before it happens

_____ historic   letters that come before the rest of the word

_____ -cooked   before recorded history

_____ dict   get ready for something before it happens

Taking it further   Look up these prefixes in a dictionary, and list all the words that start with **un-, super-, pre-**.

Suffixes

- Write the -ful suffix at the end of these words. Then cover each word and write it in full.
  (Note: there is only one l at the end of the suffix!)

beauti_____	_____	full of thanks
wonder_____	_____	full of beauty
grate_____	_____	making you stressed
dread_____	_____	very bad
stress_____	_____	making you delighted
delight_____	_____	full of wonder

- Now match each word to its meaning.

-less means without

- Write -ful and -less at the end of these words.

- Then choose from the words to describe these pictures.

-ful	-less
use_____	use _____
colour_____	colour_____
care_____	care _____
power_____	power_____
help_____	help _____

_____ _____ _____ _____ _____

What you need to know How to use suffixes to make new words.
A suffix is a group of letters that can be added to the end of a word to change its meaning.

6

Adjectives ending in -ible

- Listen carefully to the sound of words that end in -ible.
- Write the -ible suffix at the end of these words. Then cover each word and write it in full.

poss_____ _____ horr_____ _____

ed_____ _____ sens_____ _____

- Choose from the words above to fill the spaces.

If you can do something, it is _____.

It isn't _____ to run across the street.

The ghost gave a _____ scream.

Chocolate is _____ but paper is not.

Jolly Joke

What did one ghost say to the other?

Don't spook until you're spooken to!

Adjectives ending in -able

- Listen carefully to the sound of words that end in -able.
- Write the -able suffix at the end of these words.

comfort_____ fashion_____ enjoy_____ valu_____

- Now finish these sentences with your own words.

My most comfortable clothes are _____ .

My most fashionable clothes are _____ .

My most enjoyable holidays are _____ .

My most valuable possessions are _____ .

Taking it further Make lists of more words ending in **-ful**, **-less**, **-ible**, **-able**. If you have an electronic dictionary, it may allow you to look up words by their endings.

Changing y to i

Happy, happier, happiest

When you add an ending to words that end in y, you change the y to i and add the ending.

- Add suffixes to make more adjectives and nouns.

	add -er	add -est	add -ness
happy	_____	_____	_____
weary	_____	_____	_____
tidy	_____	_____	_____
silly	_____	_____	_____

Using -er, -est, -ness words

- Choose words from above to finish these sentences.

The old woman's _____ seemed
to get worse when she heard the bad news.

Even at school Emma was tidy – she was
always the _____ girl in the class.

They were the _____ days of my life.

My brother's silly, but your brother's
even _____.

What you need to know How to add endings to words.
Words that end in **y** usually change to **i** when you add an ending like **-er**, **-est**, **-ness**, **-ly**, **-es**, **-ed**.
The only exception is when you add **-ing**.

Carry, carries, carried

- Follow the same spelling rule for these verb endings.

	add -es	add -ed
carry	_____	_____
hurry	_____	_____
try	_____	_____
cry	_____	_____
reply	_____	_____

scurry
scurries
scurried

Jolly Joke

What's an eight-letter word that has one letter in it?

An envelope!

- Choose words from above to finish these sentences.

Nasima has not yet _____ to my letter.

My baby brother _____ when he is hungry.

Every morning, Dad _____ downstairs to collect the post.

Joseph cannot swim very well yet, but he always_____ hard.

Hurrying and carrying

The only time you don't change y to i is when you add -ing.

dry
drying

- Add -ing to these words.

carry	_____
hurry	_____
try	_____
cry	_____
reply	_____
supply	_____

Taking it further Collect words that end in **y**, and list them under headings of adjectives, verbs, and nouns. Nouns like 'daisy' and 'nanny' also change to **i** when you make them plural.

Double letters

**If a word has a long vowel sound in the middle, it will have a single consonant before the ending, like taping or hoping.
If a word has a short vowel sound in the middle, it will have a double consonant before the ending, like tapping and hopping.**

● Read these sentences aloud, and then ring the right spellings.

Mel was taping/tapping her favourite programme.

A branch kept taping/tapping against the window.

It was pasta for diner/dinner.

The diner/dinner enjoyed his meal and paid his bill.

At Christmas, holy/holly is used as a decoration.

A church is a holy/holly place.

Root words

● Finish filling in the root words that these longer words came from.

tape	taping	Long vowel, remove the last e
tap	tapping	Short vowel, double the last consonant
	hoping	
	hopping	

This will help you work out the spelling rules!
Write them in the table.

What you need to know   How and when to use double letters to spell words.
If a word has a long vowel sound (e.g. take), you take off the e and add the ending.
If a word has a short vowel sound (e.g. hop), you double the last consonant and add the ending.

10

Tinny or tiny?

- Write **n** or **nn** in all these words.

It was a lovely su _____y day in Ju_____e. The sun had been

shi_____ing all morning and Mr Penny was getting quite

ta _____ed as he pru _____ed his gooseberry bush. He hummed

a fu_____y little tu_____e and smiled as he noticed the

ti_____y berries begi_____ing to grow. Last year his

gooseberries had made delicious wi _____e, and he was a first

prize wi_____er in the Garden Produce Show.

* Remember: is the vowel sound long or short?
- Now read the story aloud.

Jolly Joke

What do you get when you bake a cake in a pan?

Pancakes!

Baking or backing?

If the last consonant is k you follow the same spelling rule, but instead of writing kk you write ck.

- Match these labels to their pictures.

  (Backing the car)

  (No smoking)

  (Baking the car)

  (A poisonous snake)

  (No smocking)

  (A poisonous snack)

Taking it further   Make a list of all the words where one consonant or double consonants before the ending have different meanings, e.g. fury boots or furry boots.

Greek and Latin

The ancient Greeks had a different alphabet from us. Their **f** sound was spelt **ph**. So any word with **ph** probably comes from Greek roots. ('Tele-phone' means distant sound – although the Greeks didn't actually have telephones!)

- Write the words for the objects in these pictures, and check their meanings in a dictionary.

_____   _____   _____

ch as in echo

In the Greek alphabet, their **k** sound was spelt **ch**.

- Write labels for these pictures, and check their meanings in a dictionary.

_____   _____   _____

What you need to know   How to identify everyday words from other languages to provide clues for spelling. Word origins are interesting! These two pages give you clues about which words come from Greek or Latin roots.

uni, bi, tri

Other words in the English language come from Latin, the language of the ancient Roman Empire. You can find Latin roots in words that we use for one, two, three.

unicycle

bicycle

tricycle

Jolly Joke

How do you start a flea race?

Flea-two-one-GO!

One, two, three

- Fill in the explanation for all these words.

A unicycle has one _____.

A unicorn has one _____ .

A bicycle has two _____.

You look through binoculars with two _____.

A tricycle has three _____ .

A tripod has three _____.

A triangle has three _____.

Triplets mean three _____.

Taking it further   Look in a good dictionary to find the origins of more Greek and Latin words. What does 'rhododendron' mean? Which languages does 'television' come from?

Homophones

What are homophones?

Homophones are words that have the same sound, but are spelt differently, to show they mean different things. ('Homophone' comes from Greek roots, and means 'same sound'.)

- Fill in the rest of this grid.

to	a common short word
	a number
	as well
there	a word describing a place
	belonging to them
	short for 'they are'

Which spelling?

- Cross out the words that don't make sense in these sentences.

  I had to write/right a thank-you letter.

  There is a break/brake on my bike.

  It's grate/great to see you!

  Please have a peace/piece of cake.

  Our shorts tie at the waste/waist.

  Which/witch DVD do you like best?

What you need to know   How to distinguish between the spelling and meanings of common homophones. Homophones are words that sound the same but are spelt differently, because they have different meanings. Often you have to stop and think which spelling is right for your meaning – or check in a dictionary!

These are all tricky pairs of words that sound the same but mean different things.

- Check the words in a dictionary, then write a sentence for each one to show its meaning.

which _____

witch _____

wait _____

weight _____

waste _____

waist _____

Jolly Joke

What happens if you see identical witches?

You can't tell which witch is which!

Tricky vowels

- Do the same thing for these pairs.

peace _____

piece _____

break _____

brake _____

great _____

grate _____

Taking it further   Often homophones are different parts of speech, for example **write** is a verb and **right** is an adjective. How about **passed** and **past**? Whenever you need to spell homophones you aren't sure of, it may help if you work out what part of speech each one is.

Speech marks

There are three ways of showing what people say, when you're writing.

1 Speech bubbles

2 Drama text

Brown cow: How now!

Black cow: How now to you too!

3 Speech marks

The brown cow said,
"How now!" and the black
cow replied, "How now to
you too!"

Highlight the speech

- In this passage, highlight all the parts that people say in one colour. Highlight all the parts that report what they said in another colour.

The teacher asked, "Which is farther away – China or the sun?"

"China," answered Milly.

"Why do you think that?" asked the teacher in surprise.

"Well, you can see the sun, but you can't see China," Milly replied.

- What punctuation is used within the speech marks?

- When do you start new lines? _____

What you need to know   How to write speech in three different ways.
Speech marks are the most common way of punctuating speech in children's writing.

From speech bubbles to speech marks

- Rewrite the speech bubbles as text with speech marks.

Look back to the teacher's conversation with Milly on page 16 if you need to.

How's my singing coming on, Miss Jones?

I think you should be on TV, Sam.

_____

_____

Really? You mean I'm good enough for that?

No, but if you were on TV I could switch it off!

_____

_____

Rules for speech marks

1 Start each new speaker on a new line, if it is a new sentence.

2 Put speech marks round the words actually spoken.

3 Place punctuation connected with the direct speech inside the speech marks.

4 If direct speech is followed by more text, end with a **comma**, not a full stop inside the speech marks.

Jolly Joke

Why couldn't the pirate play cards?

Because he was sitting on the deck!

Taking it further Look carefully at how direct speech is written in books. The punctuation is quite tricky to get right!

Apostrophes

Apostrophes for ownership

If someone owns something, we use an apostrophe for the owner.

the dog's bone

the cat's tail

● Now rewrite these using apostrophes.

the stripe of the zebra _____

the neck of the giraffe _____

the broom of the keeper _____

Plural owners

If there are more owners, the apostrophe goes after the s.

the zebras' stripes

the giraffes' necks

● Rewrite these with apostrophes. Check how many owners!

the bones of the dogs _____

the stripes of the tiger _____

the spots of the ladybirds _____

the spots of the ladybird _____

What you need to know How to use an apostrophe.
You use an apostrophe to indicate who is the owner. If there is only one owner, you put the apostrophe before the **s**.
If the owners end in plural **s**, you put the apostrophe after the **s**.

No apostrophes for plural nouns!

You only use an apostrophe for the owner or owners, never for ordinary plural nouns.

- Put a tick or cross to show which of these are right or wrong.

The queen's ☐ cat's ☐ were yowling in the yard.

We had burger's ☐ and chips ☐ at Ian's ☐ party.

The farmer's ☐ potatoes ☐ were stored in sack's ☐ .

Hundred's ☐ of people were at the ship's ☐ launch.

Apostrophes for missing letters

Remember that apostrophes are also used to show missing letters.

- Fill in the blanks.

Short form	Long form	Letters missed out
haven't	_____	_____
_____	does not	_____
couldn't	_____	_____
would've	_____	_____
_____	did not	_____
_____	might have	_____
_____	I have	_____
we'll	_____	_____
you're	_____	_____
_____	it is	_____

Jolly Joke

What part of English are boxers good at?

Punch-uation!

Taking it further   Look out for apostrophes in adverts and posters. Say whether they are for ownership or for missing letters. Are they always right? You can often spot errors in handwritten and printed signs.

Hyphens and brackets

Hyphens are little links that stick words together.
break-in   lay-by   mother-in-law

- Sometimes you can't be sure if words have hyphens, so check all these in the dictionary. Which need hyphens?

grandmother   _____

headphones   _____

greataunt   _____

takeaway   _____

laidback   _____

carryout   _____

Dashes

Dashes look a bit like hyphens, but dashes are used to keep parts of sentences apart.
Dashes are longer than hyphens — as you can see! You should not use dashes too often.

- Add dashes where they are needed.

Punctuation can be difficult at least I think so.

Hyphens and dashes are for different things obviously!

My joined-up writing lets me down or so my teacher says.

What you need to know   How to use hyphens, dashes and brackets.
Hyphens are used for joining words; dashes for keeping words apart; and brackets for separating off a whole phrase.

Brackets

Brackets fence off part of a sentence (like this).

But look where the full stop goes!

- Rewrite these sentences with brackets instead of **commas**.

My grandmother remembers the Second World War, 1939–1945.

_____

James, my cousin's father, married June, our neighbour's brother.

_____

Jolly Joke

What gets bigger and bigger as you take more away from it?

A hole!

Fill the gap

- Put in the hyphens, dashes, or brackets. You decide!

William Shakespeare ☐ 1564–1616 ☐ was England's greatest poet and playwright. He was born in Stratford ☐ upon ☐ Avon, the son of a well ☐ to ☐ do glove ☐ maker ☐ an important man in the town. At 18, William married a local girl ☐ Ann Hathaway ☐ but soon left Stratford to seek his fortune in London ☐ England's capital city.

Taking it further Look out for these trickier kinds of punctuation. You will see plenty of dashes in adverts. Brackets can be useful, too, as long as you get the punctuation right – usually no punctuation goes inside the brackets.

Adverbs

Adverbs give extra information about verbs.

This dog is growling playfully.

This dog is growling fiercely.

The adverbs, playfully and fiercely, tell us more about how the dog is growling.

Adverbs very often end in -ly.

Fill the gaps

- Choose adverbs to fill these gaps.

  The cat walked _____ across the steep roof.

  People talk _____ in a library.

  Matthew stroked his pet rabbit _____ .

  The cars raced _____ around the track.

  The old man spoke _____ to the dog who
  had just trampled on his flowers.

What you need to know   How to use adverbs.
Adverbs add information to verbs, saying how, when or where something happened. They make a piece of writing more interesting.

The adverb game

- With a partner, take it in turns to think of an adverb, e.g. noisily, and then do different things in the style of that adverb. The other person has to guess which adverb you have thought of.

- Another way of playing this game is for the other person to set you tasks, which you then act out in the style of the adverb you thought of. They then try to guess your adverb.

Jolly Joke

When is the vet busiest?

When it rains cats and dogs!

Adjectives and adverbs

- Add adjectives (to describe the nouns) and adverbs (to extend the verbs), to make these sentences more interesting.

The boy made his bed.

_____

The dog was growling.

_____

The monster roared.

_____

Taking it further Look at some more adverts, and try and spot the adjectives and adverbs that make the descriptions sound more tasty or irresistible.

Proofread your work

1   While you're writing, think about the meaning of what you're trying to say.

2   When you've finished, read it aloud to see if it makes sense. Check the punctuation, to see if the message comes over clearly.

3   Check the spelling. Mark any word you're not sure about, and look it up in a dictionary or spellchecker.

4   Show your work to a friend, as it can be easier to spot someone else's mistakes.

Check your spelling

- Do these words look right to you?
  Check their spellings and write in any corrections.

notice   _____

because   _____

easyly   _____

barly   _____

holyday   _____

polite   _____

What you need to know   How to check for errors after writing.
If you are writing something on-screen, it is very easy to correct your errors and improve your work.

Proofreader needed!

- Correct this newspaper advert.

CAKE CRISIS – SHOCK HORROR

All readers will know Mr jones newtowns popular baker. Mr Jones has a problem he hasent got enyone to mind his shop when he gose on holiday nexed week. if he doesent find someone there will be no bred or cakes on sale all week if you wood like to take over mr jones's shop plees right to him at 11 High street, newtown.

Beat the spellchecker

Sometimes your spellchecker won't catch the error, because the word is spelt right but used with the wrong meaning.

- Correct these sentences.

They said their were no more buns.

Hear they come, as fast as they can.

Write as rain, my mother always said.

Taking it further   Look out for misspellings in newspapers. Despite proofreaders and spellcheckers, some errors still creep through!

Myths and metaphors

Greek myths are stories that have been passed down to us from the ancient Greeks, who lived about 3000 years ago.

- Use a dictionary to find the meanings of these different kinds of ancient stories.

  Legend _____

  Fable _____

  Myth _____

Characters from myths

The characters in Greek myths were often gods who had come to live on Earth. Here are descriptions of three characters from a well-known Greek myth.

Echo: a nymph, which means a goddess of nature. She talked too much, and so was made to stop talking. From then on she could only repeat things other people said, which is why we use the word 'echo' to mean a repeated sound.

Narcissus: the boyfriend of Echo. He was very vain, which is how we get the word 'narcissistic', meaning a vain person.

Hera: the queen of gods. She was the person who cast the spell on Echo.

What you need to know Greek myths have had a lot of influence on our familiar stories. Their use of similes and metaphors has also influenced our use of poetic language.

These are two more terms that it is useful to know about.

Simile means when we compare something to something else.

Echo talked so much that it was like a river rushing on and never stopping.

Metaphor means when we say something is something else.

Echo's talking was a river in full flow, rushing on and never stopping.

- Write a simile and then a metaphor to describe Narcissus's vanity.

Simile

_____

Metaphor

_____

Jolly Joke

What do clouds wear under their clothes?

Thunderwear!

Tell the story

- On a separate sheet of paper, try writing your own story of Echo and Narcissus.

Use similes and metaphors to describe your main characters.

Think about why Hera cast the spell on Echo.

How do you think Narcissus reacted when Echo could only repeat what he said?

Taking it further Find more Greek myths to read. Can you see what influence they have had on the stories we tell each other about people's characterisics?

Why do echoes happen?

Sound is caused by vibration. This could be the vibrations in someone's windpipe when they talk, or the vibrations that happen when two heavy objects hit each other. Every sound has vibrations as its starting point. The vibrations move outwards in waves from the starting point.

Sound waves can travel through air and water. They can even travel through solid things like iron, wood or the ground. They travel out in all directions from the starting point – just like ripples on a pond. If a sound wave reaches your ear, you hear the sound.

Sometimes a sound wave travelling through air or water hits something solid, so that some of the wave bounces back and starts to travel in the opposite

Sound waves travel outwards from the starting point just like the ripples which spread out over a pond after you have thrown in a pebble.

direction. If this reflected sound wave reaches your ear, you hear an echo.

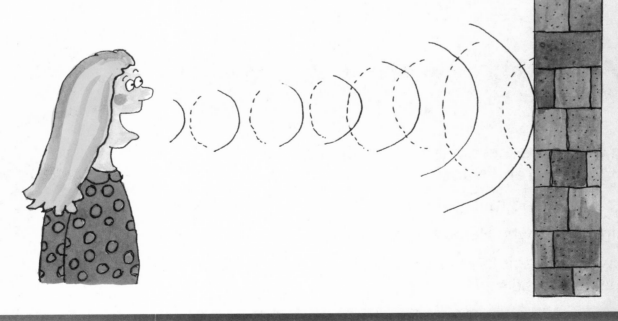

What you need to know   How non-fiction differs from fiction.
Although the theme running through pages 26–31 is echoes, the non-fiction here has a very different purpose, a different kind of language, and a different illustration style from fiction or poetry.

28

1 What causes sound?

_____

2 In what direction does sound travel?

_____

3 What can sound travel through?

_____

4 What happens when sound hits something solid?

_____

5 Have you ever heard an echo?

Yes ☐   No ☐

6 If so, what material was the sound bouncing back from?

_____

Jolly Joke

Why do you always find things in the last place you look?

Because when you have found it you stop looking!

Taking it further   Look at children's books on science. Think about what subjects they are explaining. What kind of language do they use? What 'signposts' do they use in the text, e.g. subheadings, labels and captions?

Reading poetry

● Read this poem to yourself, and then read it aloud.

The splendour falls on castle walls
And snowy summits old in story –
The long light shakes across the lakes
And the wild cataract leaps in glory.
Blow, bugle, blow, set the wild echoes flying!
Blow, bugle – answer, echoes,
      dying... dying... dying.

O hark, O hear! how thin and clear,
And thinner, clearer, farther going!
O sweet and far from cliff and scar
The horns of Elfland faintly blowing!
Blow, let us hear the purple glens replying –
Blow, bugle – answer, echoes,
      dying... dying... dying.

Alfred, Lord Tennyson (1809–1892)

What you need to know This poem is about echoes, but the style of text is totally different from fiction or non-fiction.

Explaining the poem

The poem was written over 100 years ago.

- Find out the meaning of these words.

  splendour _____   summits _____

  cataract _____   bugle _____

  glens _____

- Which lines rhyme in each verse?

  _____ and _____ ; _____ and _____

Understanding the poem

- The poem is about a boy playing the bugle in the open air. Describe the landscape in your own words.

  _____

  _____

- The poet hears echoes of the bugle bouncing back. Name four hard things in the poem that could be returning the echoes.

  1 _____   2 _____

  3 _____   4 _____

- What do you think the poet means by Elfland? Do you think it's real, or imaginary?

  _____

- How would you describe the mood of the poem? Does it seem happy or sad to you? Say why.

  _____

Taking it further   Read other poems from the nineteenth century. Do you find the language difficult? Do you learn things you couldn't learn from more modern poetry? Read contemporary poets as well, and see which you prefer.

Answers

Page 4
Un- means not
unfastened, untrue, unlucky, untidy, ungrateful

Choosing un- words
untidy, unfastened, ungrateful, unlucky, untrue

Page 5
Super- means big
superstore, superhero, supernatural, supervise
superstore, superhero, supernatural, supervise

Pre- means before
prepare – get ready for something before it happens
prefix – letters that come before the rest of the word
prehistoric – before recorded history
pre-cooked – food cooked before you plan to eat it
predict – say what will happen before it happens

Page 6
-ful means full of
beautiful – full of beauty
wonderful – full of wonder
grateful – full of thanks
dreadful – very bad
stressful – making you stressed
delightful – making you delighted

-less means without
useful, colourful, careful, powerful, helpful
useless, colourless, careless, powerless, helpless
powerful, useless, colourful, helpless, careless

Page 7
Adjectives ending in -ible
possible, horrible, edible, sensible
possible, sensible, horrible, edible

Adjectives ending in -able
comfortable, fashionable, enjoyable, valuable
Possible answers:
My most comfortable clothes are my jeans.
My most fashionable clothes are my T-shirts.
My most enjoyable holidays are at the seaside.
My most valuable possessions are my CDs.

Page 8
Happy, happier, happiest
happier, happiest, happiness
wearier, weariest, weariness
tidier, tidiest, tidiness
sillier, silliest, silliness

Using -er, -est, -ness words
weariness, tidiest, happiest, sillier

Page 9
Carry, carries, carried
carries, carried
hurries, hurried
tries, tried
cries, cried
replies, replied
replied, cries, hurries/hurried, tries

Hurrying and carrying
carrying, hurrying, trying, crying, replying, supplying

Page 10
Taping or tapping?
Ring these words: taping, tapping, dinner, diner, holly, holy

Root words
hope – long vowel, remove the last e
hop – short vowel, double the last consonant

Page 11
Tinny or tiny?
sunny, June, shining, tanned, pruned, funny, tune, tiny, beginning, wine, winner

Baking or backing?

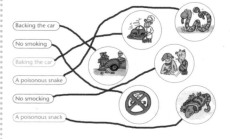

Page 12
ph as in telephone
microphone, megaphone, photograph

ch as in echo
echo, school, chemist

Page 13
One, two, three
wheel, horn, wheels, eyes, wheels, legs, sides, babies

Page 14
What are homophones?
to, two, too, there, their, they're

Which spelling?
Cross out: right, break, grate, peace, waste, witch

Page 15
Tricky w
Possible answers:
I was given an apple which I ate.
The witch rode around on her broomstick.
I had to wait for the bus.
I ate too many cakes so I put on weight.
If you write smaller you won't waste so much paper.
Her waist was very small so she needed a shorter belt.

Tricky vowels
Possible answers:
All was peace and quiet when the children went to sleep.
She cut everyone a piece of pie.
If you drop the plate on the floor it will break.
He slowed down on his bicycle by putting on the brake.
I had a great time at the fair as I won several prizes.
They burned some logs in the grate.

Page 16
Highlight the speech
Parts that people say: "Which is farther away – China or the sun?", "China,", "Why do you think that?", "Well, you can see the sun, but you can't see China,"
Parts that report: The teacher asked, answered Milly, asked the teacher in surprise, Milly replied
Punctuation used: ? ,
Start a new line when another person begins to speak.